Marley & Me

Marley to the Rescue!

HarperCollins*Publishers*

This is Marley.

He is a very friendly
and silly dog.

Marley has lots of fun when he breaks things and makes a mess. Look at Marley play with his toy on the sofa!

John and Jenny are Marley's owners.

They got Marley when he was

just a little puppy.

They love him

even when he is bad.

Marley is a member of the family.

Marley really likes the

newest member of the family.

His name is Patrick.

Marley and his family

live in a yellow house.

Marley likes the girl who lives next door. Her name is Lisa. Marley likes to chew on Lisa's trainers!

One day, Marley hears something
that makes him growl
at the window.
A girl outside yells for help.

Everyone dashes outside.

It's getting dark.

"Call the police," says John.

Jenny is worried.

John and Marley find
the girl in trouble
close to their house.
It is Lisa!
A bad man grabbed her
and stole her purse.
She was very scared.

John sits down with Lisa
for a while
and makes her feel better.
"It's okay. I've got you,"
says John.

John is so upset Lisa was hurt,

he does not notice

when he drops Marley's lead.

Oh, no!

The dog is gone!

Where can he be?

"Marley! Marley?" yells John.

WHOOP! WHOOP!
Soon, the police come
to help Lisa.

Who is in the backseat of the police car?
It is Marley!

"That is our dog!

We are sorry

if he got in your way," says John.

John and Jenny think Marley

has been bad again.

"We would not have found
the thief without him!"
says the policeman.
"This dog followed the smell
of the robber to the gas station.
He kept the man cornered
until we arrived!"

"What a good dog!" says John.

"Yes, he is!" says the officer.

"Woof!" agrees Marley.

Hooray, Marley!

You've saved the day!